Sometimes sad? Someti
deepest thoughts on pap
filling in its various char
track of your triumphs,
with the added bonus th
of them.

*My Secret File* is a private dossier that allows you to really let off steam. If you're going through a patch of loathing your friends, hating your teachers or feeling sick with yourself, you'll find a page here that relates exactly to how you feel. Not that this is a book for bad moods only. There are plenty of opportunities for blowing your own trumpet – for example, there's a Conceit Sheet where you can tell the world how great you are.

*My Secret File* is your permanent place for private information. You'll wonder what you ever did without it!

# MY SECRET FILE

JOHN ASTROP

PUFFIN BOOKS

PUFFIN BOOKS

Published by the Penguin Group
Penguin Books Ltd, 27 Wrights Lane, London W8 5TZ, England
Viking Penguin, a division of Penguin Books USA Inc.
375 Hudson Street, New York, New York 10014, USA
Penguin Books Australia Ltd, Ringwood, Victoria, Australia
Penguin Books Canada Ltd, 2801 John Street, Markham, Ontario, Canada L3R 1B4
Penguin Books (NZ) Ltd, 182–190 Wairau Road, Auckland 10, New Zealand

Penguin Books Ltd, Registered Offices: Harmondsworth, Middlesex, England

First published 1982
20  19  18  17  16  15  14  13

Printed in England by Clays Ltd, St Ives plc
Set in Linotron Baskerville

# WARNING!

Larger-type persons daring to read this book do so at the risk of shocked amazement and serious mental disturbance!

I, .........................................................., disclaim all responsibility for the ghastly results of their idle curiosity.

# MY VITAL STATISTICS

| | |
|---|---|
| HEIGHT | |
| WEIGHT | |
| HAIR COLOUR | |
| EYE COLOUR | |
| NECK SIZE | |
| CHEST SIZE (Try holding your breath) | |
| WAIST SIZE (Stop holding your breath) | |
| INSIDE LEG SIZE (Stop giggling) | |
| SHOE SIZE | |
| COUNT TOES (There should be about ten) | |

Mark in on diagram, current cuts, bruises, breaks, scabs, gnat bites, moles, inkstains and plookies (or whatever you call nasty red spots).
Add hair, wings, halo, and anything else to make this a perfect portrait of 'angelic' you.

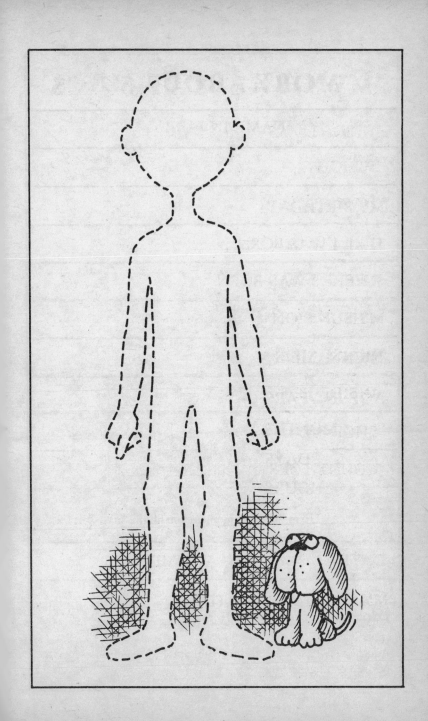

# MORE ABOUT ME

NAME IN FULL

MY BIRTHDAY

TIME I WAS BORN

WHERE I WAS BORN

MY SUN SIGN

NICKNAME/S

AGE IN YEARS

MONTHS

DAYS

HOURS

(Up to the exact moment you fill this in)

DATE                    TIME

MY BEST HANDWRITING
(Write 'my best handwriting')

# MY BABY PHOTO

## MY FINGERPRINT

## MY LIP-PRINT

## MY BLOODSTAIN
(Wait for the next accident)

## LOCK OF HAIR
(Just a little fixed with Sellotape)

MUM'S MUM

MUM'S DAD

DAD'S MUM

DAD'S DAD

MUM

DAD

# MY FAMILY
Stick in photos where possible and write names in panels.

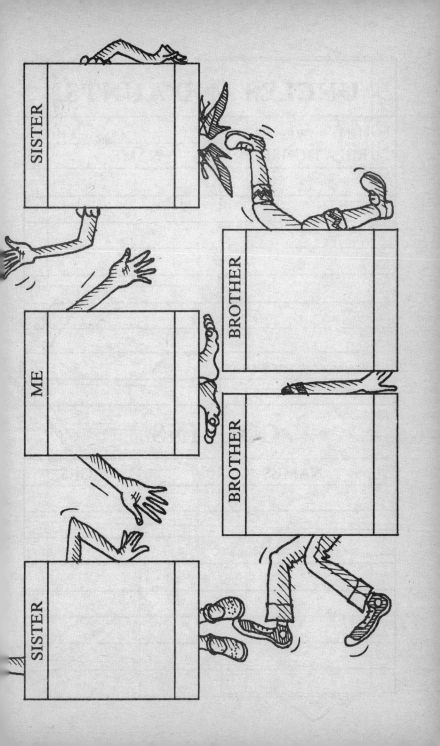

# UNCLES AND AUNTS

(ie, Mum's sister/brother, etc.)

| RELATIONSHIP | NAME |
|---|---|
|  |  |
|  |  |
|  |  |
|  |  |
|  |  |
|  |  |
|  |  |
|  |  |
|  |  |

# COUSINS

| NAMES | AGES |
|---|---|
|  |  |
|  |  |
|  |  |
|  |  |
|  |  |
|  |  |
|  |  |
|  |  |

# DISTANT RELATIONS

Remote great-aunts, third cousins, etc. Anyone that is related to you – famous, infamous, odd or eccentric.

| RELATIONSHIP | NAME | COMMENTS |
|---|---|---|
| | | |
| | | |
| | | |
| | | |
| | | |
| | | |
| | | |

# MUM'S STATISTICS

FULL NAME

NAME BEFORE SHE MARRIED

BIRTHDAY

AGE

HEIGHT

WEIGHT

HAIR COLOUR

EYE COLOUR

OCCUPATION

Draw your best picture of Mum in the frame opposite.

MUM

# MUM AS I SEE HER

She looks her best when

She looks her worst when

Her greatest talents are

1

2

Her greatest weaknesses are

1

2

Her favourite activity is

Her biggest dislike is

Her greatest fears are

1

2

She nags me most about

Ideally, she'd like me to be

She treats my friends

[ ]

The thing that makes her happiest is

[ ]

The thing that bores her most is

[ ]

I feel closest to her when

[ ]

I feel detached from her when

[ ]

She enjoys talking about

[ ]

She worries about

[ ]

The thing I can do that pleases her most is

[ ]

The thing she can do that pleases me most is

[ ]

When she's cross, I can get round her by

[ ]

When I'm in a bad mood she

[ ]

Our best shared activity is

[ ]

Underline all the words that fit Mum perfectly.
If you don't know the meanings, ask Mum and underline HELPFUL.

| | |
|---|---|
| PRIZE-WINNER | CLOCK-WATCHER |
| BAD LOSER | CRIME-DETECTOR |
| EARLY RISER | SECRET-KEEPER |
| LATE WAKER | TEAR-SHEDDER |
| FAST TALKER | GAME-PLAYER |
| SLOW THINKER | SCHOOL-HELPER |
| SNAPPY DRESSER | STORY-TELLER |
| BIG SPENDER | GOOD COOKER |
| PLEASURE-SEEKER | RECIPE-RUINER |
| FAULT-FINDER | HEALTH-FOODER |
| RULE-MAKER | CONSTANT DIETER |
| LAW-BREAKER | SWEET-FORBIDDER |
| CAKE-BAKER | HOME-DECORATOR |
| CAR-DRIVER | ANIMAL-LOVER |
| LATE ARRIVER | PEACE-MAKER |

| | | |
|---|---|---|
| CLEVER | MUSICAL | CUDDLY |
| BRILLIANT | STUDIOUS | MODEST |
| SLOW | FAT | BOASTFUL |
| STEADY | PLUMP | SHOWY |
| CAUTIOUS | SKINNY | FANCIFUL |
| PANICKY | SLIM | NOISY |
| EXCITABLE | SPORTY | QUIET |
| CALM | INVENTIVE | TALENTED |
| EFFICIENT | NEAT | ARTISTIC |
| MUDDLED | UNTIDY | PRACTICAL |
| GLOOMY | HONEST | STRONG |
| STRICT | DARING | GENTLE |
| AMUSING | SOCIABLE | CRITICAL |
| BUSY | PEACEFUL | CHATTY |
| NAGGING | FIERCE | COMIC |
| EASY-GOING | OBSTINATE | BOSSY |
| TIRED | HELPFUL | CONFIDENT |
| GOSSIPY | CRAZY | SHY |
| FORGETFUL | WORRIED | STINGY |

# DAD'S STATISTICS

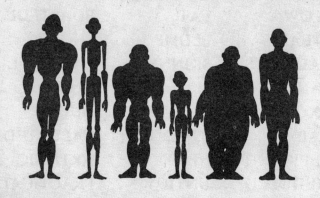

| | |
|---|---|
| FULL NAME | |
| BIRTHDAY | |
| AGE | |
| HEIGHT | |
| WEIGHT | |
| HAIR COLOUR | |
| EYE COLOUR | |
| OCCUPATION | |

Draw your best picture of Dad in the frame opposite.

DAD

# DAD AS I SEE HIM

He looks his best when

He looks his worst when

His greatest talents are

1

2

His greatest weaknesses are

1

2

His favourite activity is

His biggest dislike is

His greatest fears are

1

2

He nags me most about

Ideally, he'd like me to be

He treats my friends

The thing that makes him happiest is

The thing that bores him the most is

I feel closest to him when

I feel detached from him when

He enjoys talking about

He worries about

The thing I can do that pleases him the most is

The thing he can do that pleases me the most is

When he's cross, I can get round him by

When I'm in a bad mood he

Our best shared activity is

Underline all the words that fit Dad perfectly.
If you don't know the meanings, ask Dad and underline HELPFUL.

| | |
|---|---|
| PRIZE-WINNER | CLOCK-WATCHER |
| BAD LOSER | CRIME-DETECTOR |
| EARLY RISER | SECRET-KEEPER |
| LATE WAKER | TEAR-SHEDDER |
| FAST TALKER | GAME-PLAYER |
| SLOW THINKER | SCHOOL-HELPER |
| SNAPPY DRESSER | STORY-TELLER |
| BIG SPENDER | GOOD COOKER |
| PLEASURE-SEEKER | RECIPE-RUINER |
| FAULT-FINDER | HEALTH-FOODER |
| RULE-MAKER | CONSTANT DIETER |
| LAW-BREAKER | SWEET-FORBIDDER |
| CAKE-BAKER | HOME-DECORATOR |
| CAR-DRIVER | ANIMAL-LOVER |
| LATE ARRIVER | PEACE-MAKER |

| | | |
|---|---|---|
| CLEVER | MUSICAL | CUDDLY |
| BRILLIANT | STUDIOUS | MODEST |
| SLOW | FAT | BOASTFUL |
| STEADY | PLUMP | SHOWY |
| CAUTIOUS | SKINNY | FANCIFUL |
| PANICKY | SLIM | NOISY |
| EXCITABLE | SPORTY | QUIET |
| CALM | INVENTIVE | TALENTED |
| EFFICIENT | NEAT | ARTISTIC |
| MUDDLED | UNTIDY | PRACTICAL |
| GLOOMY | HONEST | STRONG |
| STRICT | DARING | GENTLE |
| AMUSING | SOCIABLE | CRITICAL |
| BUSY | PEACEFUL | CHATTY |
| NAGGING | FIERCE | COMIC |
| EASY-GOING | OBSTINATE | BOSSY |
| TIRED | HELPFUL | CONFIDENT |
| GOSSIPY | CRAZY | SHY |
| FORGETFUL | WORRIED | STINGY |

# SISTERS

| |
|---|
| NAME |
| AGE |
| BIRTHDAY |
| BEST POINTS |
| WORST POINTS |
| WE HAVE FUN WHEN |
| SHE ANNOYS ME WHEN |
| I ANNOY HER WHEN |
| SHE'S BETTER THAN ME AT |
| I'M BETTER THAN HER AT |

| |
|---|
| NAME |
| AGE |
| BIRTHDAY |
| BEST POINTS |
| WORST POINTS |
| WE HAVE FUN WHEN |
| SHE ANNOYS ME WHEN |
| I ANNOY HER WHEN |
| SHE'S BETTER THAN ME AT |
| I'M BETTER THAN HER AT |

# SISTERS

| | |
|---|---|
| NAME | |
| AGE | |
| BIRTHDAY | |
| BEST POINTS | |
| WORST POINTS | |
| WE HAVE FUN WHEN | |
| SHE ANNOYS ME WHEN | |
| I ANNOY HER WHEN | |
| SHE'S BETTER THAN ME AT | |
| I'M BETTER THAN HER AT | |

# BROTHERS

| | |
|---|---|
| NAME | |
| AGE | |
| BIRTHDAY | |
| BEST POINTS | |
| WORST POINTS | |
| WE HAVE FUN WHEN | |
| HE ANNOYS ME WHEN | |
| I ANNOY HIM WHEN | |
| HE'S BETTER THAN ME AT | |
| I'M BETTER THAN HIM AT | |

| | |
|---|---|
| NAME | |
| AGE | |
| BIRTHDAY | |
| BEST POINTS | |
| WORST POINTS | |
| WE HAVE FUN WHEN | |
| HE ANNOYS ME WHEN | |
| I ANNOY HIM WHEN | |
| HE'S BETTER THAN ME AT | |
| I'M BETTER THAN HIM AT | |

# BROTHERS

| | |
|---|---|
| NAME | |
| AGE | |
| BIRTHDAY | |
| BEST POINTS | |
| WORST POINTS | |
| WE HAVE FUN WHEN | |
| HE ANNOYS ME WHEN | |
| I ANNOY HIM WHEN | |
| HE'S BETTER THAN ME AT | |
| I'M BETTER THAN HIM AT | |

# MUM'S PARENTS

GRANDMA'S NAME

BIRTHDAY

GRANDPA'S NAME

BIRTHDAY

THEIR ADDRESS

TELEPHONE NUMBER

WHAT I LIKE ABOUT GRANDMA IS

WHAT I LIKE ABOUT GRANDPA IS

I SEE THEM EVERY

# DAD'S PARENTS

GRANDMA'S NAME

BIRTHDAY

GRANDPA'S NAME

BIRTHDAY

THEIR ADDRESS


TELEPHONE NUMBER

WHAT I LIKE ABOUT GRANDMA IS


WHAT I LIKE ABOUT GRANDPA IS


I SEE THEM EVERY

# MY PETS

| NAME | AGE | KIND OF ANIMAL |
|------|-----|----------------|
|      |     |                |
|      |     |                |
|      |     |                |
|      |     |                |

The best thing about pets is

I would like a

If you haven't a pet fill in your imaginary menagerie. For instance:

| ETHEL | 99 | WARTHOG |
|-------|----|---------|
|       |    |         |

| COLOURS | MAIN FOODS |
|---|---|
|  |  |
|  |  |
|  |  |
|  |  |
|  |  |
| PINK & YELLOW | BUBBLE GUM & INK— |
|  |  |

# MY HOME

**ADDRESS** Woodbine Cottage, Middle Spring, Ruscombe Stroud Glos GL6 6DF

**KIND OF HOME**

**NUMBER OF ROOMS**

**MY FAVOURITE ROOM**

**GARDEN, OR WINDOW-BOX?**

Draw a picture of your home on the page opposite.

Underline any of the following words that seem to suit your home.

| | | |
|---|---|---|
| NEAT | COLD | CLEAN |
| TIDY | OLD | LONELY |
| SCRUFFY | MODERN | TERRACED |
| CROWDED | ANTIQUE | DRIPPING TAPS |
| ROOMY | FRIENDLY | LEAKY ROOF |
| EMPTY | DETACHED | SQUEAKY DOORS |
| COLOURFUL | NOISY | DRAUGHTY HALL |
| GLOOMY | QUIET | NOISY PLUMBING |
| HISTORIC | COSY | CREAKY STAIRS |
| TINY | LUXURIOUS | CEILING CRACKS |
| PLAIN | GLOSSY | PEELING PAINT |
| WARM | UNUSUAL | SAGGING SHELVES |

**MY HOME**

# MY ROOM

The colour of the walls is

The colour of the paintwork is

Underline below the best descriptions of your room.

IMPECCABLY TIDY       MILDLY MUDDLED

DELICATELY FRILLY       OCCASIONALLY ORDERLY

HIGHLY POLISHED       A RUBBISH DUMP

HOPELESSLY CLUTTERED    AN ART GALLERY

DINGILY DIRTY       A FUN FACTORY

CREATIVELY COLOURFUL    A MADHOUSE

Draw a plan of your room (as seen from above).
Draw in bed (or beds if sharing), cupboards, door, windows, chest of drawers, etc.

# MY IDEAL ROOM

Colour of walls

Colour of paintwork

Type of bed

Kind of storage space

Gadgets



Other fantastic equipment



Draw a plan of your ideal room, the ideal bed, gadgets, entertainments and comforts.

# MY LOCALITY

Draw a map of your neighbourhood, marking friends' houses, favourite shops, school, secret places and best playing areas. Mark each place with a letter and fill in the key opposite.

**A) MY HOUSE**

**B)**

**C)**

**D)**

**E)**

**F)**

**G)**

**H)**

MY LOCALITY

# MY CLOTHES

My favourite outfit for lounging around

The three things I most hate wearing

The clothes I'd really like would be

# MY POSSESSIONS

My most valuable possession

My favourite possession

Number of board games

The best one

Number of books I own

My best collection

Number of items in collection

The most useful thing I've got

The most useless thing I've got

My oldest possession

My best thing to share with others

# POCKET MONEY

| |
|---|
| How much I get each week |
| How much I'd like to get |
| Now a serious answer |
| Mostly I spend it on |
| Number of days it lasts |
| Any saved? |
| Why not? |
| If I had £100 I'd buy |

# THE CONCEIT SHEET

This is the absolute and unbelievable best of me. On these pages I can tell the world just how really great and talented I am.

## I AM THE WORLD'S GREATEST

## I WILL UNDOUBTEDLY BECOME

## I AM UNBEATABLE AT

## MY PERSONAL APPEARANCE IS

## THE BEST OF MY GREAT BEAUTY IS MY

## PEOPLE GASP WITH AMAZEMENT AT MY

## MY KNOWLEDGE IS OUTSTANDING IN

## I'M OVERWHELMINGLY HELPFUL TO

## I MAKE LIFE MORE PLEASANT FOR

## MY GREATEST ADMIRER IS

## *MY MOST UNUSUAL ABILITY IS

|  |
|--|
|  |

## EVERYONE LOVES ME FOR MY

|  |
|--|
|  |

## THE WORLD WOULD BE A BETTER PLACE IF EVERYONE WERE AS

|  |
|--|
| AS ME!!!! |

## A FEW OF MY EVER-GROWING LIST OF TALENTS

| 1 |  |
|---|--|
| 2 |  |
| 3 |  |
| 4 |  |

*This will include such brilliant things as touching your toes with your nose, reading upside down (either you or the book), cutting the most crooked bread slices, etc.

# THE VILE FILE

This is the appalling and repelling side of me. A chance to 'come clean' and tell the world just how awful I really am. I may not even tell the truth, I'm that bad.

### I AM THE WORLD'S WORST

### I SHALL PROBABLY END UP AS A

### ALMOST EVERYONE IS BETTER THAN ME AT

### MY PERSONAL APPEARANCE IS

### THE WORST OF MY DREARY LOOKS IS MY

### PEOPLE GASP WITH HORROR AT MY

### MY BRAIN IS PEA-SIZE WHEN I HAVE TO

### I'M A LOAD OF TROUBLE TO

### I MAKE LIFE MORE DIFFICULT FOR

# *MY MOST OBJECTIONABLE TALENT IS

## MOST PEOPLE CAN'T STAND MY

## THE WORLD WOULD BE AN EVEN MORE GHASTLY PLACE IF EVERYONE WERE AS

AS ME!!!!

## A FEW OF MY EVER-GROWING LIST OF FAILURES

| | |
|---|---|
| 1 | |
| 2 | |
| 3 | |
| 4 | |

*Ugh! This can include picking scabs, speaking with a mouthful of cake crumbs, leaving smelly socks behind cupboards and other such disgusting habits.

# THE DREAD SPREADS

On these pages I make known the horrid, frightening, boring, unpleasant things that I could do very well without.

## THINGS I HATE LOOKING AT

## THINGS I COULD NEVER TOUCH

## THINGS I COULDN'T BEAR TO DO

# THE DREAD SPREADS

## THINGS THAT TERRIFY ME

## THINGS THAT IRRITATE ME

Wasps

# THINGS THAT FRUSTRATE ME

# THINGS THAT EMBARRASS ME

# THE RAGE PAGE

When you're furious, in a mad blinding rage, frustrated at the unfairness of this 'orrible world, put a big heavy tick against the reason for your fury.

| |
|---|
| DAD DID IT |
| MUM DID IT |
| BROTHER DID IT |
| SISTER DID IT |
| TEACHER DID IT |
| MY FRIEND DID IT |
| THE DOG DID IT |
| THE CAT DID IT |
| THE WEATHER DID IT |
| EVERYBODY DID IT |
| I DON'T KNOW WHO DID IT |
| I DID IT |
| NOBODY DID IT |
| I'M JUST CROSS |

Now, in complete privacy, hiss out all the words on the next page until you feel better. Whew!

| | |
|---|---|
| FOUL! | ABOMINATION! |
| UNFAIR! | OUTRAGEOUS! |
| DIRTY TRICK! | LOUSY! |
| ROTTEN DEVIL! | PUTRID! |
| SLIMY TOAD! | SICKENING! |
| ANNOYING CREEP! | REVOLTING! |
| BIG BULLY! | DAMNED! |
| BOSSY! | BLASTED! |
| BRUTAL! | NASTY! |
| UNKIND! | SORDID! |
| MEANY! | POISONOUS! |
| SPOILSPORT! | AWFUL! |
| SLUG! | TREACHEROUS! |
| STINKER! | CRAFTY! |
| BEASTLY! | PHONY! |
| PESTILENT! | FALSE! |
| SWINDLING! | DISGUSTING! |
| CROOKED! | SICK! |
| SKUNK! | NAUSEOUS! |
| CRINGING! | BIG-HEADED! |
| GRUESOME! | LOATHSOME! |
| SINISTER! | SCOWLING! |
| DREADFUL! | NAGGING! |
| RAT-FACED! | TWIT! |

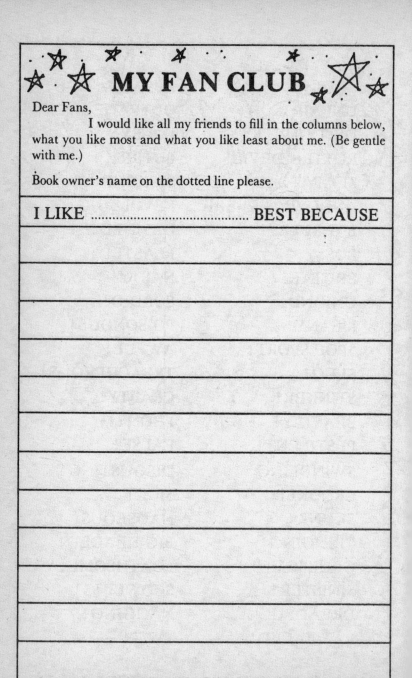

# ☆ ☆ MY FAN CLUB ☆ ☆

Dear Fans,

      I would like all my friends to fill in the columns below, what you like most and what you like least about me. (Be gentle with me.)

Book owner's name on the dotted line please.

| I LIKE .............................................. BEST BECAUSE |
|:---|
| |
| |
| |
| |
| |
| |
| |
| |
| |
| |
| |
| |

| BUT I DON'T LIKE | SIGNED |
| --- | --- |
| | |
| | |
| | |
| | |
| | |
| | |
| | |
| | |
| | |
| | |
| | |

# THE BORING
# NAG COUNT

Add a tick each time 'you know who' excel themselves with the originality of their reprimands!

You seem to think we're *made* of money! ☐

What time do you call *this?* ☐

You do *nothing* to help in the home! ☐

You're not going out until you've . . . ☐

I'm not spending money on rubbish like that! ☐

I don't care who's got one *you're* not having one! ☐

You'll sit there till you *do* eat it! ☐

If you don't clear up your room I'll . . . ☐

Why can't *you* behave like . . . ☐

What *do* you think you look like! ☐

You spend *far* too much time stuck in front of that 'box'! ☐

Why don't you *do* something! ☐

I'm not here to go around clearing up after *you!* ☐

You don't stick at *anything* for more than five minutes! ☐

I don't know what you *do* with your pocket money! ☐

I'm not having your head stuck in a comic every mealtime! ☐

Of course you won't be bored, there's plenty to do at . . . ☐

I don't care if you *are* bored, we're going and that's that! ☐

There it is, right in front of your nose, you just *don't* look!

You go about in a dream!

Time enough for that sort of thing when you're older!

For goodness sake, act your age!

Turn that ghastly row down!

Well, we want to watch *this* programme, not *that* horrible rubbish!

I'm not waiting on *you* hand and foot!

You'll be grateful to us for making you do it . . .

Wait till you have to go out and earn a living, then you'll . . .

Stop putting ticks in that book every time I speak!

# CONFESSIONS

Add a tick for each 'orrible offence.

| THE DEADLY DEED | |
|---|---|
| I deliberately lied. | |
| I got a friend into trouble. | |
| I smashed something on purpose. | |
| I told tales on somebody. | |
| I gave away a secret. | |
| I stole something. | |
| I cheated at school. | |
| I bullied someone. | |
| I spoilt someone else's work. | |
| I didn't own up to something I'd done. | |
| I took credit for something I hadn't done. | |
| I took more than my fair share. | |
| I didn't help someone when I could have. | |
| I was rude to someone. | |
| I fiddled the change from shopping. | |
| I teased someone for pleasure. | |
| I didn't fill in my confessions truthfully. | |

# THE THINNEST

| EVENT | RECORD SET |
|---|---|
| The greatest length of time I can suck a Polo | |
| The most number of times I can fold a sheet of paper | |
| The shortest time in which I can get dressed | |
| The longest I can go without saying a word (only when awake) | |
| The longest I've stayed in bed | |
| The furthest I can throw a cotton-wool ball | |
| The largest number of words I can make using the letters from my full name | |
| My longest hum, without taking a breath | |
| The greatest number of one inch or more shreds, after unpicking a shredded wheat | |
| My fastest time for drinking a bowl of soup with the wrong end of the spoon | |
| My longest stare-battle without a blink | |
| The most socks I can get on one foot | |

# BOOK OF RECORDS

| DATE | RECORD BEATEN | DATE |
|------|---------------|------|
|      |               |      |
|      |               |      |
|      |               |      |
|      |               |      |
|      |               |      |
|      |               |      |
|      |               |      |
|      |               |      |
|      |               |      |
|      |               |      |
|      |               |      |

# MY TEN BEST BOOKS

| 1 | Lord of the Rings |
|---|---|
| 2 | |
| 3 | |
| 4 | |
| 5 | |
| 6 | |
| 7 | |
| 8 | |
| 9 | |
| 10 | |

# MY TEN MOST
# BORING BOOKS

| | |
|---|---|
| 1 | |
| 2 | |
| 3 | |
| 4 | |
| 5 | |
| 6 | |
| 7 | |
| 8 | |
| 9 | |
| 10 | |

# MY TEN BEST SINGLE RECORDS

| | |
|----|----|
| **1** | |
| **2** | |
| **3** | |
| **4** | |
| **5** | |
| **6** | |
| **7** | |
| **8** | |
| **9** | |
| **10** | |

# MY TEN WORST
# SINGLE RECORDS

| 1 | |
|---|---|
| 2 | |
| 3 | |
| 4 | |
| 5 | |
| 6 | |
| 7 | |
| 8 | |
| 9 | |
| 10 | |

# MY TEN
# FAVOURITE FOODS

| | |
|---|---|
| **1** | Fish 'n' chips and Coke |
| **2** | |
| **3** | |
| **4** | |
| **5** | |
| **6** | |
| **7** | |
| **8** | |
| **9** | |
| **10** | |

# MY TEN MOST
# HATED FOODS (UGH!)

| 1 | school mash |
|----|-------------|
| 2 | |
| 3 | |
| 4 | |
| 5 | |
| 6 | |
| 7 | |
| 8 | |
| 9 | |
| 10 | |

# MY TEN BEST
# TV PROGRAMMES

| 1 | |
|---|---|
| 2 | |
| 3 | |
| 4 | |
| 5 | |
| 6 | |
| 7 | |
| 8 | |
| 9 | |
| 10 | |

# MY TEN MOST
# YAWNMAKING TV
# PROGRAMMES

| 1 | |
|---|---|
| 2 | |
| 3 | |
| 4 | |
| 5 | |
| 6 | |
| 7 | |
| 8 | |
| 9 | |
| 10 | |

# CHRISTMAS IS COMING

## NUMBER OF DAYS TO CHRISTMAS

| | | | | | | | |
|---|---|---|---|---|---|---|---|
| 30 | 29 | 28 | 27 | 26 | 25 | 24 | 23 |
| 22 | 21 | 20 | 19 | 18 | 17 | 16 | 15 |
| 14 | 13 | 12 | 11 | 10 | 9 | 8 | 7 |
| 6 | 5 | 4 | 3 | 2 | 1 | | |

# WHAT I'D LIKE
# FOR CHRISTMAS

# CHRISTMAS CARD
# CHECK LIST

| NAME | ADDRESS | SENT |
|------|---------|------|
|      |         |      |
|      |         |      |
|      |         |      |
|      |         |      |
|      |         |      |
|      |         |      |
|      |         |      |
|      |         |      |
|      |         |      |
|      |         |      |
|      |         |      |

# WHAT I'M GOING TO GIVE FOR CHRISTMAS

| NAME | PRESENT | COST |
|------|---------|------|
|      |         |      |
|      |         |      |
|      |         |      |
|      |         |      |
|      |         |      |
|      |         |      |
|      |         |      |
|      | TOTAL   |      |

# CHRISTMAS DAY

| I woke at | Got up at |
|-----------|-----------|

We had lunch at

For lunch we had


Our visitors were

We visited

For supper we had

# MY PRESENTS

| PRESENT | WHO FROM |
|---------|----------|
|         |          |
|         |          |
|         |          |
|         |          |
|         |          |
|         |          |
|         |          |
|         |          |
|         |          |
|         |          |

# THANK-YOU LETTERS

| WHO TO | POSTED |
|--------|--------|
|        |        |
|        |        |
|        |        |
|        |        |
|        |        |

# NEW YEAR RESOLUTIONS

At this time of year masses of mad-brained people decide to give up all their bad habits, turn over a new leaf, change their wicked ways, and generally improve themselves. How about you?

### THIS YEAR I'M GOING TO STOP . . .

### THIS YEAR I'M GOING TO START . . .

# MY SCHOOL

| |
|---|
| Full name of school |
| Phone number |
| Address |
| |
| My class |
| Class teacher |
| Number in class |
| Head teacher |
| School starts at |
| School finishes at |
| EASTER HOLIDAY |
| RETURN DATE |
| HALF-TERM |
| RETURN DATE |
| SUMMER HOLIDAY |
| RETURN DATE |
| HALF-TERM |
| RETURN DATE |
| CHRISTMAS HOLIDAY |
| RETURN DATE |
| HALF-TERM |
| RETURN DATE |

# HOW I GET ON

MY BEST SUBJECT IS

MY WORST SUBJECT IS

Underline the words that fit you at school.

| | | |
|---|---|---|
| POPULAR | REBEL | PATIENT |
| HARD-WORKING | DIMWIT | HELPFUL |
| LAZY | BRAINY | SPORTY |
| DREAMY | QUICK | UNSPORTY |
| ENTHUSIASTIC | SLOW | MUSICAL |
| FORGETFUL | AVERAGE | JOKEY |
| LONELY | TOP | LEADER |
| BORED | CREATIVE | NOISY |
| STUDIOUS | GIGGLY | PERFECT |

# THE REST OF THE CLASS

Fill in names of the classmate that fits best (in code if it will keep you out of trouble).

| THE BRILLIANT BRAIN |
| THE GIGGLER |
| THE TELL-TALE |
| THE BULLY |
| THE SPORTS CHAMP |
| THE MONEY BAGS |
| THE SCRUFF |
| THE ARTIST |
| THE DUNCE |
| THE SHOW-OFF |
| THE FLIRT |
| THE CHATTERER |
| THE NERVOUS |
| THE BRAVE |
| THE CLOWN |
| THE BOSSY |

If you're not one of the above fill in *your* title below

I AM

# PARTY RATINGS

**A)** ABSOLUTELY FANTASTIC!!!
**B)** REALLY GOOD!
**C)** NOT BAD
**D)** FAIR
**E)** FAIRLY BORING
**F)** TERRIBLE
**G)** YUK!!!

| WHOSE PARTY | WHAT KIND | RATING A, B, C, ETC. |
|---|---|---|
|  |  |  |
|  |  |  |
|  |  |  |
|  |  |  |
|  |  |  |
|  |  |  |
|  |  |  |
|  |  |  |
|  |  |  |
|  |  |  |
|  |  |  |

# THE FAMILY HOLIDAY

WHEN

WHERE

HOW LONG

HOW WE GOT THERE

HOW LONG IT TOOK

DISTANCE WE TRAVELLED

THE WEATHER WAS MOSTLY

# THE RATINGS

| | 1 | 2 | 3 | 4 | 5 | 6 | 7 | 8 | 9 | 10 |
|---|---|---|---|---|---|---|---|---|---|---|
| WHOLE HOLIDAY | | | | | | | | | | |
| FOOD | | | | | | | | | | |
| TREATS | | | | | | | | | | |
| POCKET MONEY | | | | | | | | | | |
| BEST TRIP | | | | | | | | | | |
| THE JOURNEY | | | | | | | | | | |
| COMING BACK | | | | | | | | | | |

## THINGS I BROUGHT BACK

## THINGS I LOST

STiCK-iNS

# BIRTH SIGNS

Thousands of years ago our ancestors worked out a system for describing people's characters according to the time of the year they were born. If you fancy trying them out on your friends, dates and brief descriptions are below.

**Aries** the Ram    21 March to 20 April
Adventurous, enthusiastic, a bit selfish, they like winning and hate losing. They stick by their friends. Like to get things going. Good leaders.

**Taurus** the Bull    21 April to 20 May
Sometimes a bit slow and careful. Usually calm. Not quick to try out new things. Loyal friends. Good at making things work. Good at making money.

**Gemini** the Twins    21 May to 20 June
Talkative, active, can usually do more than one thing at a time. Gets the hang of things quickly. Doesn't stick at anything too long. Good company.

**Cancer** the Crab    21 June to 21 July
Close friends. They care about other people a lot. Usually have good memories. Helpful when you're in trouble. Often quite a good mimic. Good humour.

**Leo** the Lion    22 July to 21 August
Likes to be in the centre of things. Organises well but can often be bossy. Usually talented, especially at acting. Good fun. Loyal and generous friends.

**Virgo** the Virgin    22 August to 21 September
Good at organising in a quiet, efficient way. Helpful, especially remembering the bits you forgot at school. Devoted friends, but a wee bit choosy and critical.

**Libra** the Scales    22 September to 22 October
Great company. Love doing fun things with others.
Good long conversations and arguments. Sometimes
have difficulty in making up their minds.

**Scorpio** the Scorpion    23 October to 21 November
Enthusiastic and imaginative. Like to attempt the
impossible. Powerful friends and defenders, but
spiteful enemies. Good at solving problems.

**Sagittarius** the Archer
22 November to 22 December
Usually good at sporty things and going places.
Adventurous and bold. Say what they think even if
the truth hurts. Honest friends.

**Capricorn** the Goat    23 December to 20 January
Good common-sense friends. A bit cautious. Usually
good at school, so they can be helpful. Great
organisers. Usually have influential friends.

**Aquarius** the Water Carrier
21 January to 19 February
Likes new, exciting and unusual things. Good with
gadgets. Rarely shy. Usually has hordes of friends of
all kinds and ages. A bit of a rebel.

**Pisces** the Fishes    20 February to 20 March
Good imagination, sympathetic and understanding.
Another helper if you're in trouble. Good for close
friendship but gets a little swamped in a crowd.

Fill in birthdays of family, friends, pop stars, sports heroes, pets, etc. There's already one famous person for each date.

# JANUARY

| | |
|---|---|
| 1 | |
| 2 | |
| 3 | |
| 4 | |
| 5 | |
| 6 | |
| 7 | |
| 8 | |
| 9 | |
| 10 | |
| 11 | |
| 12 | |
| 13 | |
| 14 | |
| 15 | |
| 16 | |
| 17 | |
| 18 | |
| 19 | |
| 20 | |
| 21 | |
| 22 | |
| 23 | |
| 24 | |
| 25 | |
| 26 | |
| 27 | |
| 28 | |
| 29 | |
| 30 | |
| 31 | |

1 **J. EDGAR HOOVER** Founder of the F.B.I.
2 **DAVID BAILEY** British photographer
3 **J. R. R. TOLKIEN** British author of *The Lord of the Rings*
4 **JACOB GRIMM** Collector of fairy tales
5 **STELLA GIBBONS** British author of *Cold Comfort Farm*
6 **JOAN OF ARC** French saint
7 **SAINT BERNADETTE** of Lourdes
8 **ELVIS PRESLEY** American singer
9 **RICHARD NIXON** Former American president
10 **DAME BARBARA HEPWORTH** British sculptress
11 **GORDON SELFRIDGE** Founder of Selfridge's store
12 **JACK LONDON** American author of *Call of the Wild*
13 **SOPHIE TUCKER** American singer
14 **ALBERT SCHWEITZER** Doctor, humanitarian and musician
15 **PRINCESS MICHAEL OF KENT**
16 **ANDRÉ MICHELIN** French industrialist
17 **MACK SENNET** American film producer
18 **A. A. MILNE** British author of *Winnie the Pooh*
19 **PAUL CÉZANNE** French painter
20 **FEDERICO FELLINI** Italian film director
21 **BENNY HILL** British comedian
22 **LORD BYRON** British poet
23 **EDOUARD MANET** French painter
24 **BAMBER GASCOIGNE** British television presenter
25 **W. SOMERSET MAUGHAM** British writer
26 **PAUL NEWMAN** American film actor
27 **LEWIS CARROLL** British author of *Alice in Wonderland*
28 **KING HENRY VII**
29 **FREDERICK DELIUS** British composer
30 **VANESSA REDGRAVE** British actress
31 **ANNA PAVLOVA** Russian ballerina

# FEBRUARY

1
2
3
4
5
6
7
8
9
10
11
12
13
14
15
16
17
18
19
20
21
22
23
24
25
26
27
28
29

1 CLARK GABLE American film star
2 NELL GWYNNE British actress at the court of King Charles II
3 ELIZABETH BLACKWELL First woman doctor
4 CHARLES LINDBERG American aviator
5 FRANK MUIR British television personality
6 RONALD REAGAN American president
7 CHARLES DICKENS British novelist
8 JAMES DEAN American film actor
9 BRENDAN BEHAN Irish writer
10 BERTOLT BRECHT German dramatist
11 MARY QUANT British fashion designer
12 CHARLES DARWIN British naturalist
13 GEORGES SIMENON Belgian author of the Maigret stories
14 KEVIN KEEGAN British footballer
15 GALILEO GALILEI Italian astronomer
16 PETER PORTER Australian poet
17 ALAN BATES British actor
18 MARY TUDOR Queen of England
19 PRINCE ANDREW Second son of Queen Elizabeth II
20 SIDNEY POITIER American film actor
21 DUCHESS OF KENT
22 KENNETH WILLIAMS British actor
23 SAMUEL PEPYS British diarist
24 WILHELM GRIMM German collector of fairy tales
25 GEORGE HARRISON Beatle
26 BUFFALO BILL American cowboy
27 ELIZABETH TAYLOR British-born actress
28 VASLAW NIJINSKY Russian ballet dancer
29 GIOACCHINO ROSSINI Italian composer

# MARCH

| | |
|---|---|
| 1 | |
| 2 | |
| 3 | |
| 4 | |
| 5 | |
| 6 | |
| 7 | |
| 8 | |
| 9 | |
| 10 | |
| 11 | |
| 12 | |
| 13 | |
| 14 | |
| 15 | |
| 16 | |
| 17 | |
| 18 | |
| 19 | |
| 20 | |
| 21 | |
| 22 | |
| 23 | |
| 24 | |
| 25 | |
| 26 | |
| 27 | |
| 28 | |
| 29 | |
| 30 | |
| 31 | |

1 DAVID NIVEN British actor
2 D. H. LAWRENCE British writer
3 ALEXANDER GRAHAM BELL American inventor of telephone
4 PATRICK MOORE British TV personality and astronomer
5 REX HARRISON British actor
6 MICHELANGELO Italian artist
7 SIR JOHN HERSCHEL British astronomer (discoverer of Uranus)
8 KENNETH GRAHAME British author of *The Wind in the Willows*
9 BILLIE BEAUMONT British rugby player
10 PRINCE EDWARD Youngest son of Queen Elizabeth II
11 HAROLD WILSON Former British prime minister
12 MAX WALL British comedian
13 RUDOLPH NUREYEV Russian ballet dancer
14 ALBERT EINSTEIN German physicist
15 ANDREW JACKSON Former American president
16 GEORG SIMON OHM German scientist
17 KATE GREENAWAY British illustrator of children's books
18 RIMSKY-KORSAKOV Russian composer
19 DAVID LIVINGSTONE British explorer
20 SIR MICHAEL REDGRAVE British actor
21 JOHANN SEBASTIAN BACH German composer
22 MAI BRITT Swedish actress
23 MARGARET OF ANJOU English queen
24 SONIA LANNAMAN British athlete
25 KING HENRY II of England
26 DIANA ROSS American singer
27 JAMES CALLAGHAN Former British prime minister
28 MICHAEL PARKINSON British television presenter
29 ARTHUR NEGUS British antiques expert
30 VINCENT VAN GOGH Dutch painter
31 ROBERT WILHELM BUNSEN German chemist

# APRIL

| | |
|---|---|
| 1 | |
| 2 | |
| 3 | |
| 4 | |
| 5 | |
| 6 | |
| 7 | |
| 8 | |
| 9 | |
| 10 | |
| 11 | |
| 12 | |
| 13 | |
| 14 | |
| 15 | |
| 16 | |
| 17 | |
| 18 | |
| 19 | |
| 20 | |
| 21 | |
| 22 | |
| 23 | |
| 24 | |
| 25 | |
| 26 | |
| 27 | |
| 28 | |
| 29 | |
| 30 | |

1 SERGEI RACHMANINOFF Russian composer
2 PENELOPE KEITH British actress
3 DORIS DAY American singer and actress
4 MARGUERITE DURAS French novelist
5 BETTE DAVIS American film actress
6 HARRY HOUDINI American escapologist
7 DAVID FROST British television personality
8 DOROTHY TUTIN British actress
9 ISAMBARD KINGDOM BRUNEL British engineer
10 GENERAL WILLIAM BOOTH British founder Salvation Army
11 NORMAN MCLAREN British film animator
12 BOBBY MOORE British footballer
13 SAMUEL BECKETT Irish playwright
14 JULIE CHRISTIE British film actress
15 LEONARDO DA VINCI Italian artist
16 SPIKE MILLIGAN Comedy actor and writer
17 NIKITA KHRUSHCHEV Former Soviet leader
18 HAYLEY MILLS British actress
19 DUDLEY MOORE British actor and pianist
20 ADOLF HITLER German leader of the Nazi movement
21 QUEEN ELIZABETH II
22 LENIN Russian revolutionary leader
23 WILLIAM SHAKESPEARE
24 BARBRA STREISAND American singer and film actress
25 ELLA FITZGERALD American jazz singer
26 JOHN JAMES AUDUBON Haitian artist and naturalist
27 SAMUEL MORSE American inventor of the morse code
28 MIKE BREARLEY British cricketer
29 DUKE ELLINGTON American jazz composer and pianist
30 QUEEN JULIANA OF THE NETHERLANDS

# MAY

1
2
3
4
5
6
7
8
9
10
11
12
13
14
15
16
17
18
19
20
21
22
23
24
25
26
27
28
29
30
31

1 DUKE OF WELLINGTON British commander and statesman
2 BING CROSBY American singer and film actor
3 HENRY COOPER British boxer
4 AUDREY HEPBURN British actress
5 KARL MARX German philosopher and economist
6 SIGMUND FREUD Austrian founder of psychoanalysis
7 SCOBIE BREASLEY British rider
8 DAVID ATTENBOROUGH British television producer, naturalist
9 GLENDA JACKSON British actress
10 FRED ASTAIRE American tap dancer and actor
11 SALVADOR DALI Spanish surrealist painter
12 FLORENCE NIGHTINGALE Nursing reformer
13 STEVIE WONDER Blind American singer
14 ERIC MORECAMBE British comedian
15 FRANK L. BAUM American author of *The Wizard of Oz*
16 WOODY HERMAN American jazz clarinettist
17 ERIK SATIE French composer
18 DAME MARGOT FONTEYN British ballet dancer
19 LADY ASTOR First British woman MP
20 HONORÉ DE BALZAC French writer
21 HENRI ROUSSEAU French primitive painter
22 LORD OLIVIER British actor
23 FRANZ MESMER German physician and hypnotist
24 QUEEN VICTORIA
25 RICHARD DIMBLEBY Television commentator
26 JOHN WAYNE American cowboy actor
27 WILD BILL HICKOK American cowboy
28 IAN FLEMING British author of the James Bond books
29 JOHN F. KENNEDY Assassinated American president
30 CORNELIA OTIS SKINNER American humorist
31 PRINCE RAINIER III OF MONACO

# JUNE

1
2
3
4
5
6
7
8
9
10
11
12
13
14
15
16
17
18
19
20
21
22
23
24
25
26
27
28
29
30

1 **JOANNA LUMLEY** British actress
2 **SIR EDWARD ELGAR** British composer
3 **RAOUL DUFY** French painter
4 **SIR CHRISTOPHER COCKERELL** British inventor of the hovercraft
5 **MARGARET DRABBLE** British writer
6 **BJÖRN BORG** Swedish tennis player
7 **PAUL GAUGUIN** French painter
8 **ROBERT STEPHENSON** Scottish engineer
9 **COLE PORTER** American composer
10 **JUDY GARLAND** American actress and singer
11 **JACQUES COUSTEAU** French undersea explorer
12 **CHARLES KINGSLEY** British author of *The Water Babies*
13 **MIKE YARWOOD** British impersonator
14 **BURL IVES** American country singer
15 **RICHARD BAKER** British television newsreader
16 **STAN LAUREL** The thin one from Laurel and Hardy
17 **JOHN WESLEY** Founder of the Methodists
18 **PAUL MCCARTNEY** Beatle
19 **KING JAMES** I
20 **ERROL FLYNN** Australian-born film actor
21 **FRANÇOISE SAGAN** French writer
22 **PRUNELLA SCALES** British actress
23 **DUKE OF WINDSOR**
24 **JUAN MANUEL FANGIO** Racing driver
25 **CYRIL FLETCHER** British television personality
26 **LAURIE LEE** British writer
27 **HELEN KELLER** American writer though blind, deaf and mute
28 **JOHN INMAN** British comedy actor
29 **PETER PAUL RUBENS** Flemish painter
30 **SUSAN HAYWARD** American film actress

# JULY

1
2
3
4
5
6
7
8
9
10
11
12
13
14
15
16
17
18
19
20
21
22
23
24
25
26
27
28
29
30
31

JULIUS

1  PRINCESS OF WALES
2  HERMANN HESSE  German poet and novelist
3  ROBERT ADAM  British architect
4  LOUIS ARMSTRONG  American jazz trumpeter
5  JEAN COCTEAU  French writer
6  JOHN PAUL JONES  American naval commander
7  RINGO STARR  Beatle
8  JOHN D. ROCKEFELLER  American millionaire
9  BARBARA CARTLAND  British writer
10  ARTHUR ASHE  American tennis player
11  YUL BRYNNER  American actor
12  JULIUS CAESAR  Roman emperor who conquered Britain
13  JOHN DEE  Elizabethan scholar and mathematician
14  EMMELINE PANKHURST  Suffragette leader
15  INIGO JONES  British architect
16  GINGER ROGERS  American actress and tap dancer
17  ERLE STANLEY GARDNER  American thriller writer
18  W. G. GRACE  British cricketer
19  ILIE NASTASE  Rumanian tennis player
20  SIR EDMUND HILLARY  The first to conquer Mt Everest
21  JONATHAN MILLER  British doctor, and director
22  ALEXANDER CALDER  Sculptor of mobiles
23  MICHAEL FOOT  Leader of the Labour Party
24  AMELIA EARHART  Pioneer aviator
25  ELIZABETH HAMILTON  Irish writer
26  MICK JAGGER  Lead singer with the Rolling Stones
27  SHIRLEY WILLIAMS  British politician
28  BEATRIX POTTER  Writer of children's books
29  BENITO MUSSOLINI  Italian dictator
30  KATE BUSH  British singer
31  EVONNE CAWLEY  Australian tennis player

# AUGUST

1
2
3
4
5
6
7
8
9
10
11
12
13
14
15
16
17
18
19
20
21
22
23
24
25
26
27
28
29
30
31

1 HERMAN MELVILLE American writer
2 ALAN WHICKER Television presenter
3 TERRY WOGAN Irish DJ and television personality
4 QUEEN ELIZABETH THE QUEEN MOTHER
5 NEIL ARMSTRONG First man on the moon
6 LUCILLE BALL American comedienne
7 WALTER SWINBURN Irish jockey
8 RORY CALHOUN American actor
9 KING HENRY V
10 HERBERT HOOVER Former American president
11 ANGUS WILSON British novelist
12 THOMAS BEWICK British engraver
13 ALFRED HITCHCOCK British-born film director
14 JOHN GALSWORTHY British novelist
15 PRINCESS ANNE Daughter of Queen Elizabeth II
16 MENACHEM BEGIN Israeli prime minister
17 DAVY CROCKETT American pioneer
18 SHELLEY WINTERS American actress
19 OGDEN NASH American humorist
20 BERNARD O'HIGGINS Chilean patriot
21 PRINCESS MARGARET Sister of Queen Elizabeth II
22 STEVE DAVIS British snooker champion
23 GENE KELLY American actor and dancer
24 AUBREY BEARDSLEY British illustrator
25 IVAN THE TERRIBLE Russian tsar
26 FRANS HALS Dutch painter
27 SAMUEL GOLDWYN American film producer
28 WOLFGANG VON GOETHE German poet and novelist
29 JAMES HUNT British racing driver
30 MARY SHELLEY British author of *Frankenstein*
31 SIR BERNARD LOVELL British astronomer

# SEPTEMBER

1
2
3
4
5
6
7
8
9
10
11
12
13
14
15
16
17
18
19
20
21
22
23
24
25
26
27
28
29
30

1 EDGAR RICE BURROUGHS American author of *Tarzan*
2 JOHN HOWARD British prison reformer
3 CARL DAVID ANDERSON Nuclear physicist
4 JOAN AIKEN British author
5 JESSE JAMES American outlaw
6 JANE ADDAMS American social worker
7 QUEEN ELIZABETH I
8 HARRY SECOMBE Welsh singer and comedian
9 CARDINAL RICHELIEU French statesman
10 ARNOLD PALMER American golfer
11 D. H. LAWRENCE British writer
12 JESSE OWENS American athlete
13 ROALD DAHL British writer
14 PETER SCOTT Ornithologist and artist
15 PORFIRIO DIAZ Mexican dictator
16 LAUREN BACALL American film actress
17 MAUREEN CONNOLLY (Little Mo) American tennis champion
18 GRETA GARBO Swedish film star
19 DEREK NIMMO British actor
20 SOPHIA LOREN Italian actress
21 DICK TURPIN English highwayman
22 CAPTAIN MARK PHILLIPS Husband of Princess Anne
23 MICKEY ROONEY American actor
24 F. SCOTT FITZGERALD American novelist
25 FELICITY KENDAL British actress
26 GEORGE GERSHWIN American composer
27 SIR BERNARD MILES British actor and director
28 BRIGITTE BARDOT French film star
29 SEBASTIAN COE British runner
30 MARC BOLAN British singer

# OCTOBER

1
2
3
4
5
6
7
8
9
10
11
12
13
14
15
16
17
18
19
20
21
22
23
24
25
26
27
28
29
30
31

1 JULIE ANDREWS British actress and singer
2 STING Lead singer with Police
3 PIERRE BONNARD French painter
4 BUSTER KEATON Comedian in silent films
5 CHARLTON HESTON American actor
6 MELVYN BRAGG Television presenter and novelist
7 NIELS BOHR Atomic physicist
8 JUAN PERÓN Argentinian dictator
9 JOHN LENNON Beatle
10 MAGNUS MAGNUSSON Icelandic television presenter
11 ETHEL MANNIN British novelist
12 ANGELA RIPPON British newsreader
13 MARGARET THATCHER British prime minister
14 CLIFF RICHARD British singer
15 ROSCOE TANNER American tennis player
16 OSCAR WILDE Irish writer
17 RITA HAYWORTH American film star
18 MELINA MERCOURI Greek actress
19 LEWIS MUMFORD American writer
20 SIR CHRISTOPHER WREN British architect
21 GEOFF BOYCOTT British cricketer
22 SARAH BERNHARDT French actress
23 DIANA DORS British actress
24 SIR ROBIN DAY British television presenter
25 PABLO PICASSO Spanish artist
26 MAHALIA JACKSON American gospel singer
27 JOHN CLEESE British actor
28 JIMMY SAVILE British DJ and TV personality
29 JAMES BOSWELL Scottish biographer
30 LOUIS MALLE French film director
31 CHIANG KAI-SHEK Chinese nationalist leader

# NOVEMBER

| | |
|---|---|
| 1 | |
| 2 | |
| 3 | |
| 4 | |
| 5 | |
| 6 | |
| 7 | |
| 8 | |
| 9 | |
| 10 | |
| 11 | |
| 12 | |
| 13 | |
| 14 | |
| 15 | |
| 16 | |
| 17 | |
| 18 | |
| 19 | |
| 20 | |
| 21 | |
| 22 | |
| 23 | |
| 24 | |
| 25 | |
| 26 | |
| 27 | |
| 28 | |
| 29 | |
| 30 | |

1 VICTORIA DE LOS ANGELES Spanish soprano
2 BURT LANCASTER American actor
3 ADAM ANT British singer
4 KING WILLIAM III
5 LESTER PIGGOTT British jockey
6 ADOLPHE SAX Instrument maker
7 MARIE CURIE French chemist
8 KEN DODD British comedian
9 KATHARINE HEPBURN American actress
10 RICHARD BURTON Welsh actor
11 RENÉ CLAIR French film director
12 PRINCESS GRACE OF MONACO
13 ROBERT LOUIS STEVENSON Scottish writer
14 PRINCE CHARLES
15 PETULA CLARK British singer
16 TIBERIUS Roman emperor
17 FIELD-MARSHAL MONTGOMERY British soldier
18 KIM WILDE British singer
19 JODIE FOSTER American film actress
20 ALISTAIR COOKE British journalist and broadcaster
21 RENÉ MAGRITTE Belgian surrealist painter
22 BILLIE JEAN KING American tennis player
23 HARPO MARX Silent member of the Marx Brothers
24 IAN BOTHAM British cricketer
25 FRANCIS DURBRIDGE British mystery writer
26 PAT PHOENIX Elsie Tanner in 'Coronation Street'
27 ERNIE WISE British comedian
28 WILLIAM BLAKE British artist and writer
29 LOUISA M. ALCOTT American author of *Little Women*
30 SIR WINSTON CHURCHILL British statesman

# DECEMBER

| | |
|---|---|
| 1 | |
| 2 | |
| 3 | |
| 4 | |
| 5 | |
| 6 | |
| 7 | |
| 8 | |
| 9 | |
| 10 | |
| 11 | |
| 12 | |
| 13 | |
| 14 | |
| 15 | |
| 16 | |
| 17 | |
| 18 | |
| 19 | |
| 20 | |
| 21 | |
| 22 | |
| 23 | |
| 24 | |
| 25 | |
| 26 | |
| 27 | |
| 28 | |
| 29 | |
| 30 | |
| 31 | |